CODE

The Thunderbolt

Jan Burchett and Sara Vogler • Jon Stuart

Contents

OXFORD

UNIVERSITY PRESS

Macro Marvel
(billionaire inventor)

Welcome to Micro World!

Macro Marvel invented Micro World – a micro-sized theme park where you have to shrink to get in.

A computer called **CODE** controls Micro World and all the robots inside – MITEs and BITEs.

A MITE

A BITE

Disaster strikes!

CODE goes wrong on opening day.
CODE wants to shrink the world.

Macro Marvel is trapped inside the park ...

Enter Team X!

Four micro agents – **Max, Cat, Ant** and **Tiger** – are sent to rescue Macro Marvel and defeat CODE.

Mini Marvel joins Team X.

Mini Marvel
(Macro's daughter)

In the last book ...

- Cat and Mini found out about the Speed-BITE.

- Max, Ant and Rex escaped from a train as it was falling off the track!

- Ant slipped down the steel wire ...

**CODE key
(3 collected)**

You are in the Wild Rides zone.

3

Before you read

Sound checker
Say the sounds.

o   o-e

Sound spotter
Blend the sounds.

g	o	l	d

n	o	s	e

b	o	l	t	ed

l	oa	d	s

Tricky words

what
said
there

Into the zone

Can you remember why Ant
was slipping down the wire?

Fast Facts

Ant slipped down the wire.
Tiger saved him.

"Cool car! What is it?" said Ant.
"It's the Thunderbolt," Tiger
told him.

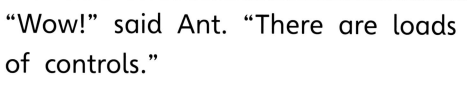

"Wow!" said Ant. "There are loads of controls."

He pressed a button.

"The screen is telling us about the Thunderbolt."

go-faster fin
bolted on

gold spokes
on wheels

The Thunderbolt

sleek shape

cone-shaped nose

"Look!" said Ant. "We have to press the red button to start the car, and press the gold button to escape from the car."

Now you have read ...
Fast Facts

Text checker

What have you found out about the Thunderbolt?

MITE fun

Which button would you press to start the car? Which button would you press to escape from the car?

I like driving the Thunderbolt!

Before you read

Sound checker

Say the sounds.

o   o-e

Sound spotter

Blend the sounds.

o	v	er

g	o	i	ng

h	o	l	e

r	o	s	e

Tricky words

said
there
have

Into the zone

Where do you think Ant and
Tiger will go in the Thunderbolt?

Out of Control

Ant and Tiger raced along in the Thunderbolt. Tiger's watch flashed. "The Speed-BITE is nearby," he said.

The Speed-BITE was on the track.
Tiger chased it.
"We'll soon find the CODE key,"
said Ant.

"Look! The track is broken!" yelled Tiger. "There's a huge hole!"

The BITE rose up in the air. It jumped over the hole and landed on the other side.

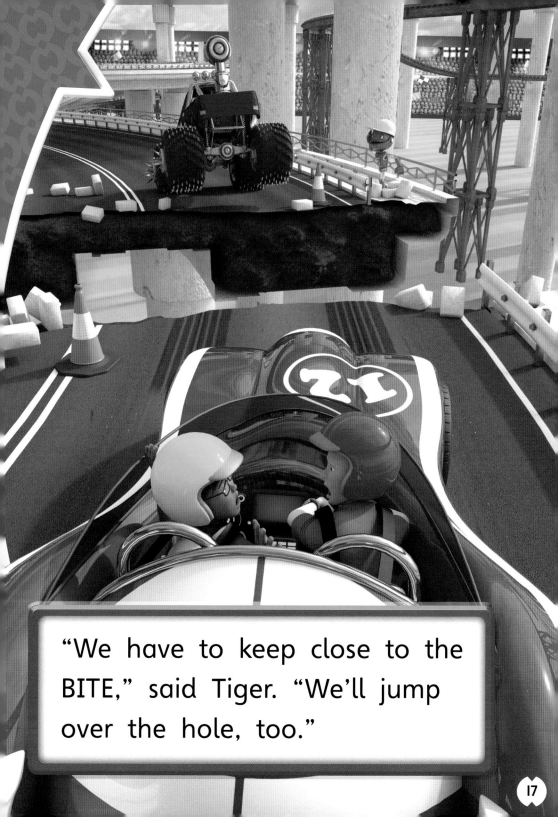

"We have to keep close to the BITE," said Tiger. "We'll jump over the hole, too."

Tiger lost control. The Thunderbolt turned over and over.

"Hold on tight!" cried Tiger.
He pressed the gold button.

Ant and Tiger shot out
of the Thunderbolt.

The Thunderbolt hit the road and exploded! MITEs put out the flames with foam.

Ant floated down and landed safely.

Tiger floated down, too. "I'm going into the BITE!" he yelled.

Now you have read ...
Out of Control

Text checker

How many words with the /oa/ sound can you find
in the story? Make a table like this:

o	o͡-e͡	oa
Thunderbolt	clo͡se	floated

MITE fun

Imagine you are shooting out of the Thunderbolt
with Ant and Tiger.
What can you hear, see, smell or touch?
How do you feel?